JUMP-START YOUR LIBRARY

Hands-on Materials for Library Learning

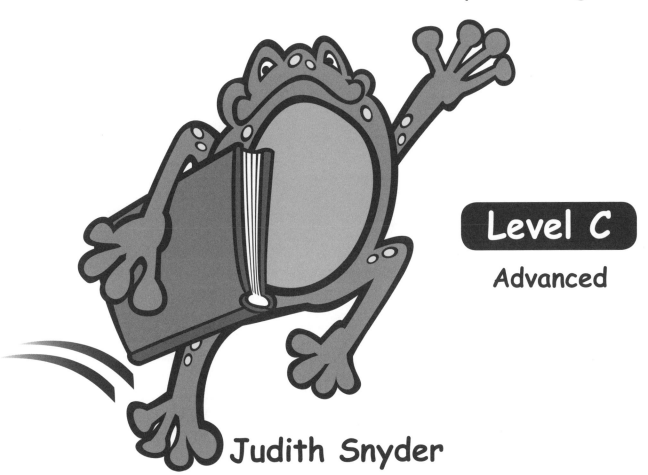

Level C

Advanced

Judith Snyder

UpstartBooks

Janesville, Wisconsin

To my son, Dr. Greg Snyder, who loves learning as much as I do.

Published by UpstartBooks
401 S. Wright Rd.
Janesville, WI 53547
1-800-448-4887

© Judith Snyder, 2008
Cover design: Deb Neu

The paper used in this publication meets the minimum requirements of American National Standard for Information Science — Permanence of Paper for Printed Library Material. ANSI/NISO Z39.48-1992.

Contents

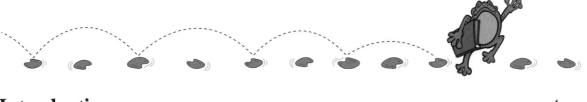

Introduction

Jump-start Your Library — Level C: Advanced reviews and extends student knowledge of how to access materials in the library. Manipulatives aid instructors in ascertaining student understanding and give students the opportunity to use several learning modalities. Instructors model the activities and guide student practice, constructively interacting on an as-needed basis. Created for large-group instruction, *Jump Start Your Library* activities can also be used in small groups. The activities may be taught on consecutive days or integrated into collaboratively planned units just prior to student application. Mastery of the skills is not expected until after students practice accessing books for several months.

The manipulatives will fit into either #10 envelopes or zip-closure plastic bags. Label the envelope or bag with the corresponding level and activity number as shown on the manipulative (C-1, C-2). Store each set in larger envelopes or boxes.

The lessons address the following Information Literacy Standards[1]:

Standard One

- The student who is information literate accesses information efficiently and effectively.

  Indicator: Develops and uses successful strategies for locating information

Standard Two

- The student who is information literate evaluates information critically and competently.

  Indicator: Selects information appropriate to the problem or question at hand

Standard Three

- The student who is information literate uses information accurately and creatively.

  Indicator: Integrates new information into one's own knowledge

Standard Nine

- The student who contributes positively to the learning community and to society is information literate and participates effectively in groups to pursue and generate information.

  Indicators: Shares knowledge and information with others. Respects others' ideas and backgrounds and acknowledges their contributions. Collaborates with others, both in person and through technologies, to identify information problems, and to seek their solutions

[1]From *Information Power: Building Partnerships for Learning*, ALA Editions, 1998.

Fiction Organization

Library Strategies

- Reviewing the difference between fiction and nonfiction
- Understanding the meaning of the letters in a fiction call number
- Alphabetizing fiction book authors to the second and third letters

Materials Needed

- overhead of Fiction/Everybody Spines (page 7)
- overhead of Author Names, cut into strips (page 8)
- Call Number card sets — one per pair of students (pages 9–11). Copy each unique set onto a different colored paper.
- two picture books and two chapter books placed on each table
- paper/pencil or white boards/dry erase markers or individual chalkboards/chalk

Time Needed

45 minutes

Directions

1. Briefly review the difference between fiction and nonfiction and show where each type of book is found in the library. Explain that today's activity will focus on how fiction books are arranged on the shelves.

2. Explain that fiction books are divided into two groups and given a letter to identify their location. The E on the spine indicates a fiction book that contains many pictures. They are called picture books or Easy books, and in some libraries are called Everybody books. The F (or Fic) stands for fiction books that are longer and have fewer pictures. Sometimes these books use more difficult vocabulary words.

3. Show overhead strips of one E and one F book spine. Identify the location of the E and F (Fic) letters on a spine label. Ask students to find the letters on the book spines at their table.

4. Lay the remaining spine overheads on the overhead screen and ask students to help you sort them into the two groups.

5. Explain that there are other letters underneath the E or F. Ask if anyone remembers what the letters mean. (The letters stand for the author's last name.)

6. Distribute white boards and markers. Display the Author Names overhead, uncovering one name at a time and ask students to write the call number for the book.

   Optional: If white boards or chalkboards are available, have students hold up their board when finished, for easy checking.

7. Explain that after fiction books are divided into E and F groups, they are placed on the shelves alphabetically by the author's last name. Review alphabetizing by the second or third letter if necessary.

8. *Optional:* Students pretend to have written a chapter book and write the call number for their book on the white board. Allow five or six students at a time to stand in order as their books would be on the shelves, holding the call number so the class can see and check their order. Ask the last group to remain standing and use a few other "authors" to place themselves into that group. Select names that will cause the class to alphabetize to the second or third letter.

9. Distribute Call Number card sets to each pair of students. The task is to arrange the call numbers as they would appear on the shelves.

10. Check progress as the pairs work, and offer support where needed. If a pair shows understanding, allow them to peruse the books on the table. Students needing additional support can be given a different set of cards to use for practice.

Teacher Tip

Easy/Everybody Section: Some libraries choose to call the picture book area the Everybody section instead of the Easy section. At the beginning of each year, I stress the varied reading levels of picture books, ranging from no words to eighth grade reading levels. This encourages all students to feel comfortable choosing these great books without feeling stigmatized. Older students with lower reading abilities feel better about choosing these books as well.

Teacher Tip

When distributing Call Number card sets, alternate the color sets to every other pair. That way, if students mix their cards up with another, the colors make it easier to sort. Because sets are different, students can exchange cards for extended practice.

Fiction/Everybody Spines

Make a transparency of this page and cut into strips.

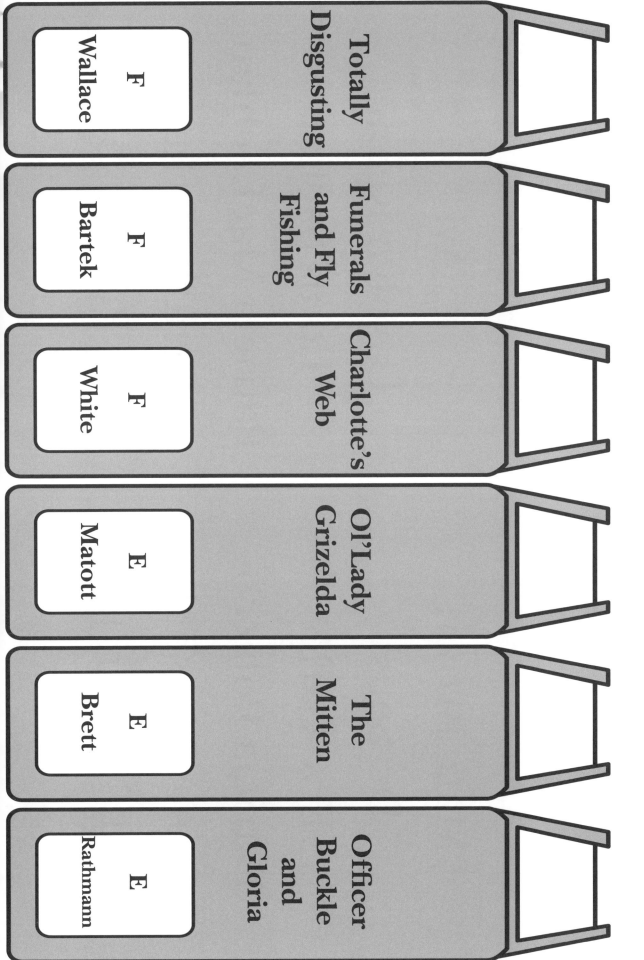

Book	Call Number
Totally Disgusting	F Wallace
Funerals and Fly Fishing	F Bartek
Charlotte's Web	F White
Ol' Lady Grizelda	E Matott
The Mitten	E Brett
Officer Buckle and Gloria	E Rathmann

Overhead of Author Names

E

Marc Brown

Dr. Seuss

Eric Carle

Patricia Polacco

James Marshall

Bill Martin, Jr.

F

Avi

Carolyn Keene

Louis Sachar

Patricia MacLachlan

Cynthia Rylant

Mary Pope Osborne

Call Number Card Set #1 for Fiction

Photocopy five of each set onto cardstock and laminate. Each set should be on different colors of paper.

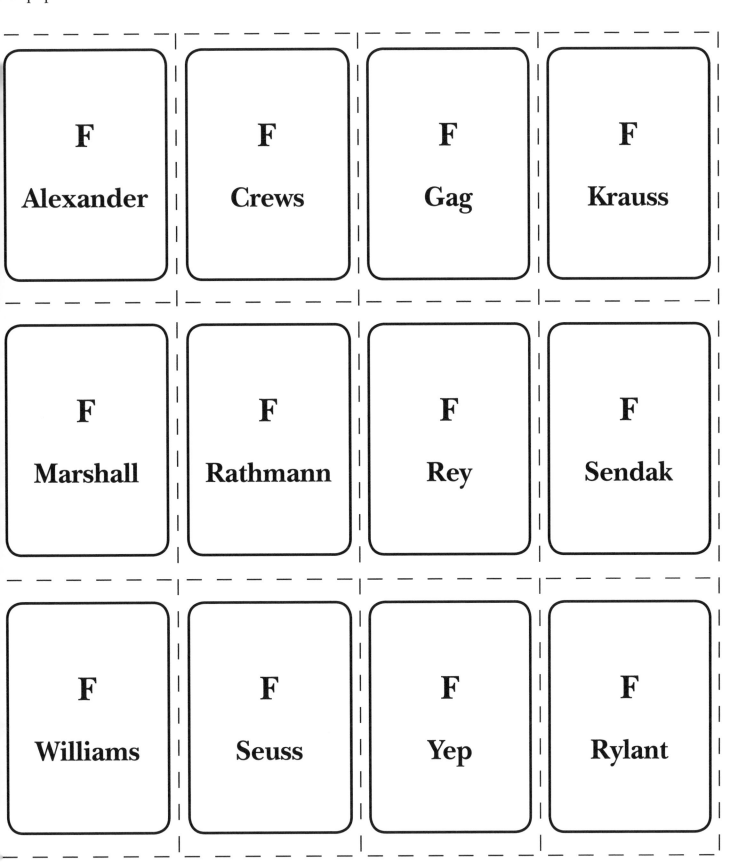

F Alexander	F Crews	F Gag	F Krauss
F Marshall	F Rathmann	F Rey	F Sendak
F Williams	F Seuss	F Yep	F Rylant

Call Number Card Set #2 for Fiction

Photocopy five of each set onto cardstock and laminate. Each set should be on different colors of paper.

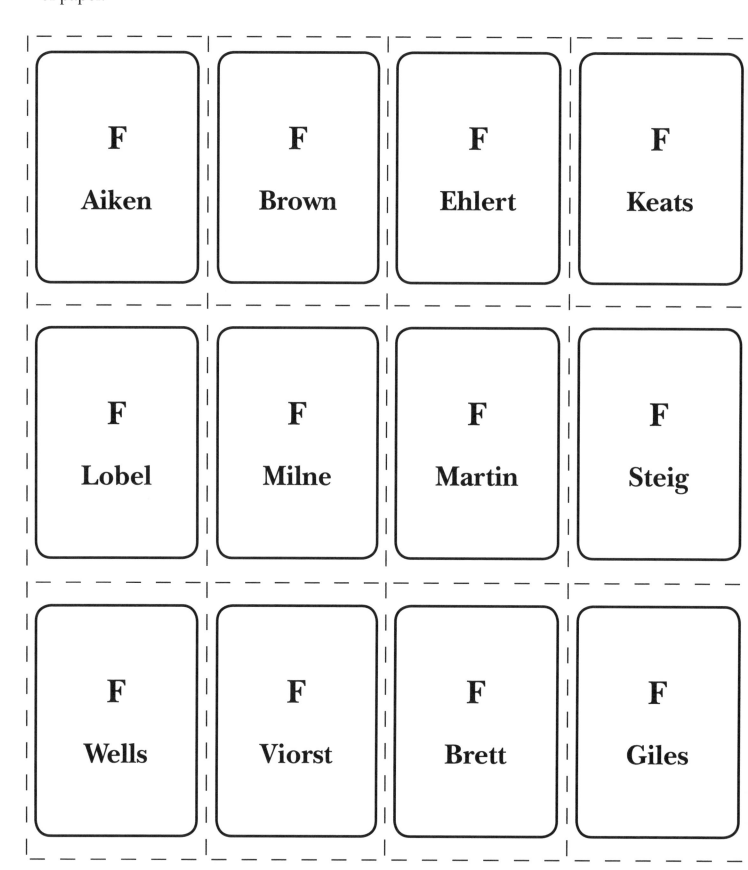

F
Aiken

F
Brown

F
Ehlert

F
Keats

F
Lobel

F
Milne

F
Martin

F
Steig

F
Wells

F
Viorst

F
Brett

F
Giles

Call Number Card Set #3 for Fiction

Photocopy five of each set onto cardstock and laminate. Each set should be on different colors of paper.

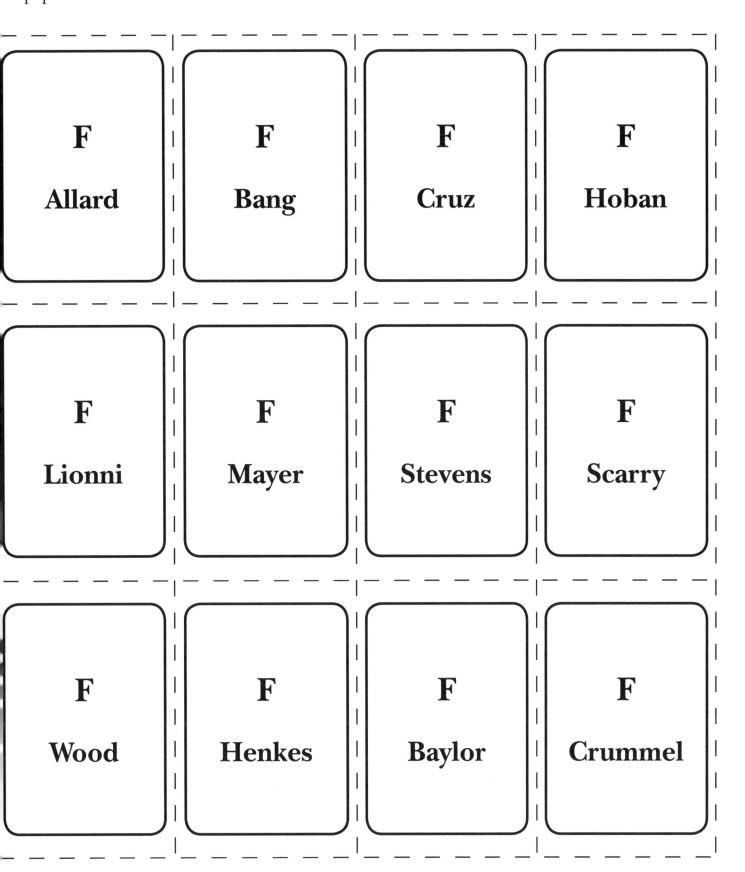

F Allard	F Bang	F Cruz	F Hoban
F Lionni	F Mayer	F Stevens	F Scarry
F Wood	F Henkes	F Baylor	F Crummel

Nonfiction Organization

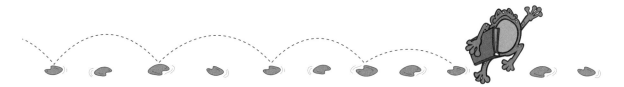

Library Strategies

- Introducing the Dewey Decimal system
- Introducing the concept that nonfiction books are categorized by subject and that each subject has a number assigned to it

Materials Needed

- Dewey Decimal Chart for each pair of students (page 13)
- Overhead of Dewey Decimal Chart (page 13)
- Book Titles list (page 14)
- Dewey Number Card Sets (page 15) in various colors

Time Needed

20–30 minutes

Directions

1. Explain that the purpose of the activity is to learn about the different subject categories in the nonfiction sections and the general hundreds number associated with it.

2. Distribute the Dewey Decimal Chart to pairs of students.

3. Display the chart on the overhead and read through the categories.

4. Give each child a Dewey Number card set. Be sure to intersperse colors for easy sorting if cards become mixed. Instruct the class to lay the cards face up on the table.

5. Using the list of book titles, read each title aloud, one at a time, giving students time to refer to the Dewey Decimal Chart and decide the title's Dewey category.

6. Students then hold up the corresponding Dewey number so the teacher/librarian can see their choice. Discuss answers. Sometimes students show very good reasoning, yet the answer is incorrect. Explain Dewey's reasoning to help them understand.

Dewey Decimal Chart

Make one overhead and one card stock copy for each student or pair of students.

Dewey Decimal Chart

000–099 Generalities
newspapers, collection of facts

100–199 Philosophy, Psychology
ideas about understanding self, feelings, ghosts, aliens

200–299 Religion
ways people worship God, Bible stories, myths

300–399 Social Sciences
communication, politics, government,
festivals, holidays, war, folktales, fairy tales

400–499 Language
dictionaries, foreign languages, books about words

500–599 Natural Sciences and Mathematics
math, earth science, weather, dinosaurs,
wild animals, plants, habitats, space

600–699 Applied Sciences
farm animals, pets, cooking, computers, cars, human body

700–799 Fine Arts
crafts, music, painting, sports, dance, comics

800–899 Literature
poetry, plays, short story collections, classic writing

900–999 Geography, History
explorers, travel, countries, history, biographies, states

Book Titles

Read each title aloud, giving students time to identify the Dewey category to which it belongs and hold up the corresponding Dewey number.

Guinness Book of World Records

Basketball for Beginners

I'm Feeling Sad

Jump Rope Poems

Ghosts: Are They Real?

All About Congress

Greek Myths

Shakespeare's Plays

Bible Stories

Meet the Orchestra

Learn Spanish

Travel to France

Rocks and Minerals

United States History

Colorado

Police and Firefighters

Italian Cooking

Cows and Sheep

Living Dinosaurs

The Arctic Ice Cap

George Washington

Mars: The Red Planet

Dewey Number Card Sets

Photocopy one set for each student onto variously colored cardstock.
Cut apart and place in baggies or small containers for storage when not in use.

000	100
200	300
400	500
600	700
800	900

Organizing Nonfiction Call Numbers

Library Strategies

- Organizing nonfiction call numbers

- Understanding that nonfiction books are sorted by the author's last name if the numbers are the same

Materials Needed

- Dewey Decimal Chart (page 13)

- overhead of Dewey Decimal Chart (page 13)

- Bookshelf overhead (page 18)

- Overhead Spine Labels for Nonfiction—cut apart (page 19)

- Large Book Spines with Nonfiction Numbers (pages 20–21)

- Nonfiction Spines Card Sets with title and call numbers—five different sets in five different colors (pages 22–31)

- magazine selection for students when work is finished

Time Needed

45 minutes

Directions

1. Place the bookshelf overhead on the projector and demonstrate how to order Dewey Decimal numbers using the overhead spine label examples. Place a few individual overhead spine labels at the bottom of the bookshelf where they can be seen.

2. Ask individual students to place the call numbers in order on the bookshelf overhead. (It helps to place two or three of the individual spine labels at the bottom of the overhead screen at a time.) Explain the meaning of the letters under the number.

3. For additional practice, ask five students to hold the large book spines at the front of the room. Ask students to put the book spines and the students holding the book spines, in order, as they would be found on the shelf. Remind the class to put the numbers in order first. Then, only if the numbers are the same, should they look at the letters of the author's last name.

4. Distribute one set of Spine Label cards to each pair of students. The task is to put the book spines in order. When students finish, allow them to turn the cards over for self checking. The sets of book spines may be traded between groups until students show understanding.

Teacher Tip

Place magazines or nonfiction books at each table for students to browse through when their work is successfully completed.

Bookshelf Overhead

Overhead Spine Labels for Nonfiction

Photocopy five of each set onto cardstock and laminate.
Each set should be on different colors of paper.

597 **Ale**	**597** **Blu**	**596** **Fre**	**595** **Ham**
523 **Tay**	**523** **Bre**	**398.2** **Mat**	**398.2** **Sim**
497 **Gre**	**497** **Gar**	**368** **Gye**	**492** **Flu**

Large Book Spines with Nonfiction Numbers

Enlarge each spine to fit on pieces of 6x18" construction paper or posterboard.

The Mitten

398.2

Brett

Weather

551.6

Juettner

American Cookbook

641.5

White

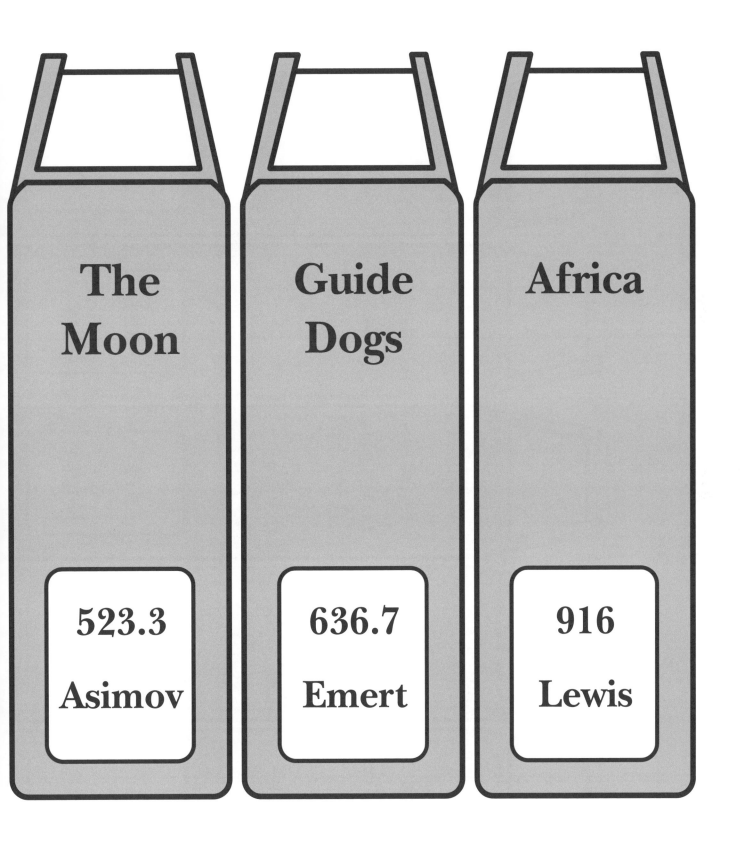

The
Moon

523.3

Asimov

Guide
Dogs

636.7

Emert

Africa

916

Lewis

Nonfiction Spines Card Set 1

Photocopy the picture on page 23 to the back of this page. Cut the spines apart. Students place the spines in order, then flip the pieces over to check their work. If the picture is correct, the spines are correct.

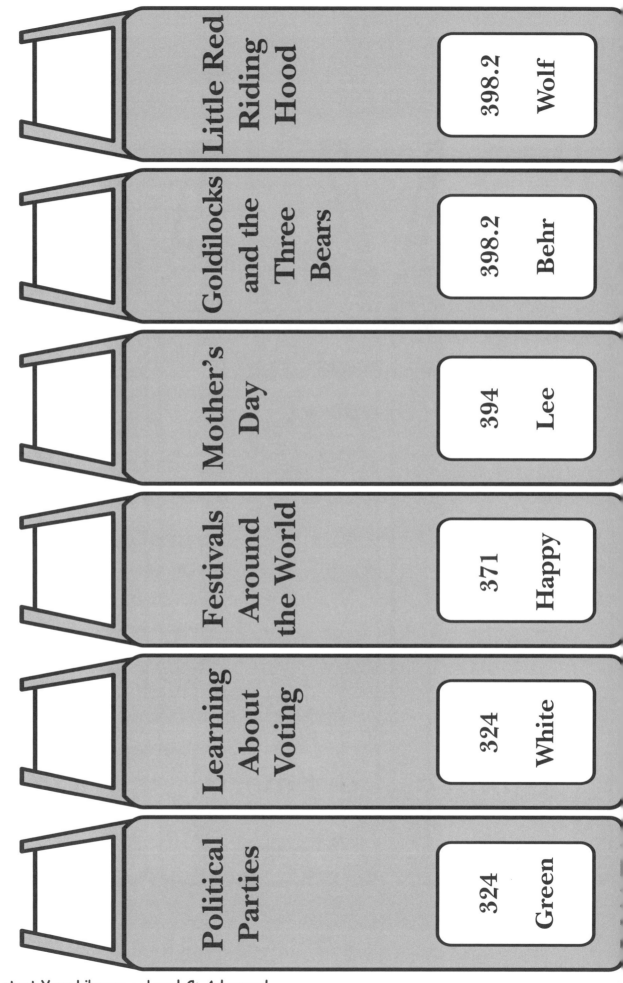

Little Red Riding Hood	398.2 Wolf
Goldilocks and the Three Bears	398.2 Behr
Mother's Day	394 Lee
Festivals Around the World	371 Happy
Learning About Voting	324 White
Political Parties	324 Green

Nonfiction Spines Card Set 1 Picture Checker

Photocopy this picture onto the back of the spine cards on the previous page.

300–399 Social Sciences

Nonfiction Spines Card Set 2

Photocopy the picture on page 25 to the back of this page. Cut the spines apart. Students place the spines in order, then flip the pieces over to check their work. If the picture is correct, the spines are correct.

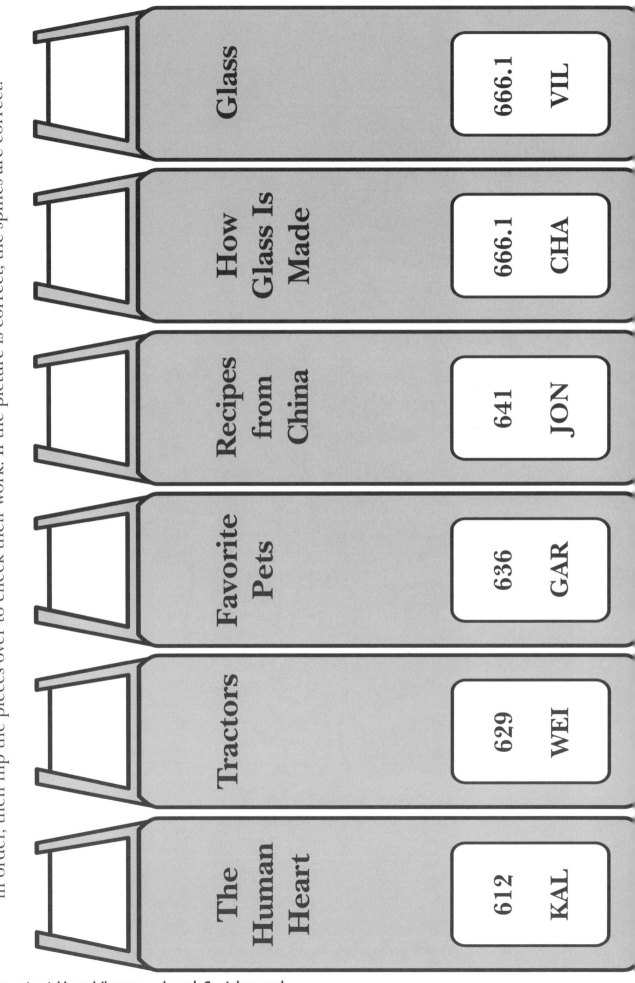

Glass	666.1 VIL
How Glass Is Made	666.1 CHA
Recipes from China	641 JON
Favorite Pets	636 GAR
Tractors	629 WEI
The Human Heart	612 KAL

Nonfiction Spines Card Set 2 Picture Checker

Photocopy this picture onto the back of the spine cards on the previous page.

600–699 Applied Sciences

Nonfiction Spines Card Set 3

Photocopy the picture on page 27 to the back of this page. Cut the spines apart. Students place the spines in order, then flip the pieces over to check their work. If the picture is correct, the spines are correct.

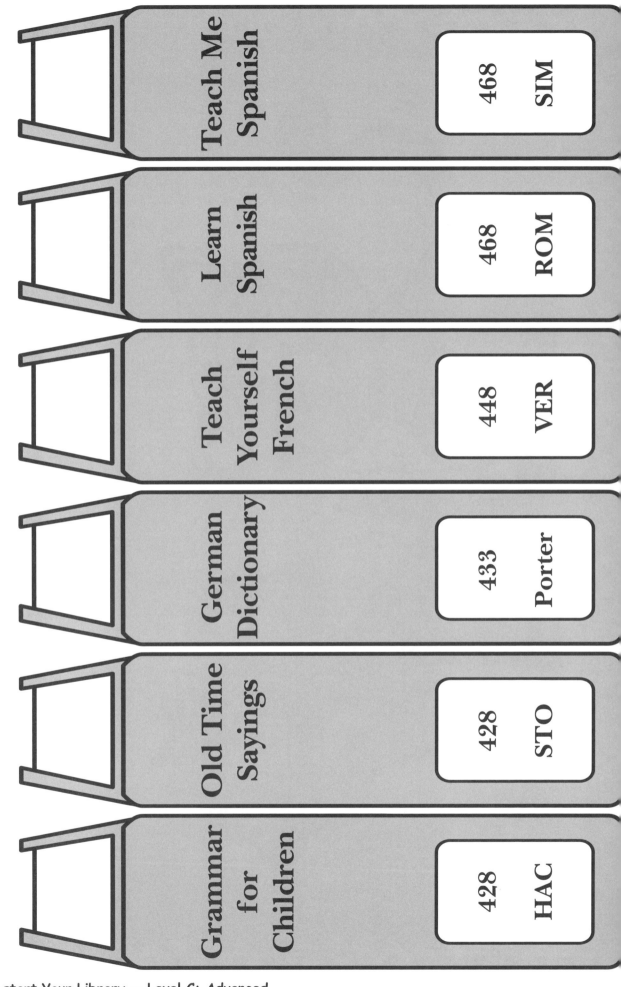

Teach Me
Spanish

468
SIM

Learn
Spanish

468
ROM

Teach
Yourself
French

448
VER

German
Dictionary

433
Porter

Old Time
Sayings

428
STO

Grammar
for
Children

428
HAC

Nonfiction Spines Card Set 3 Picture Checker

Photocopy this picture onto the back of the spine cards on the previous page.

400–499 Language

Hello Yia sou

Bonjour Ciao

Hola Guten Tag

Nonfiction Spines Card Set 4

Photocopy the picture on page 29 to the back of this page. Cut the spines apart. Students place the spines in order, then flip the pieces over to check their work. If the picture is correct, the spines are correct.

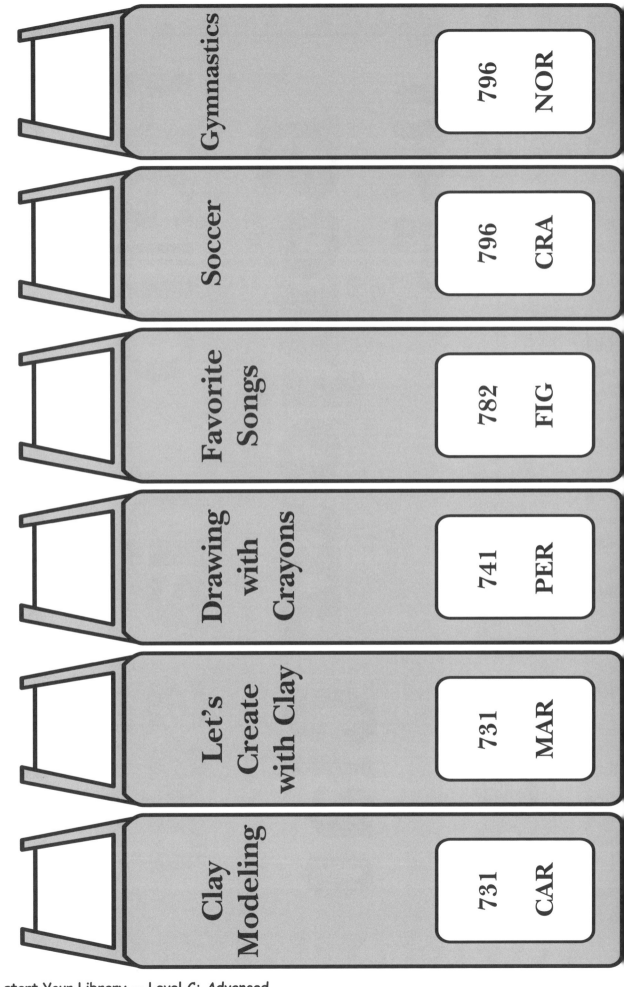

Gymnastics	796 NOR
Soccer	796 CRA
Favorite Songs	782 FIG
Drawing with Crayons	741 PER
Let's Create with Clay	731 MAR
Clay Modeling	731 CAR

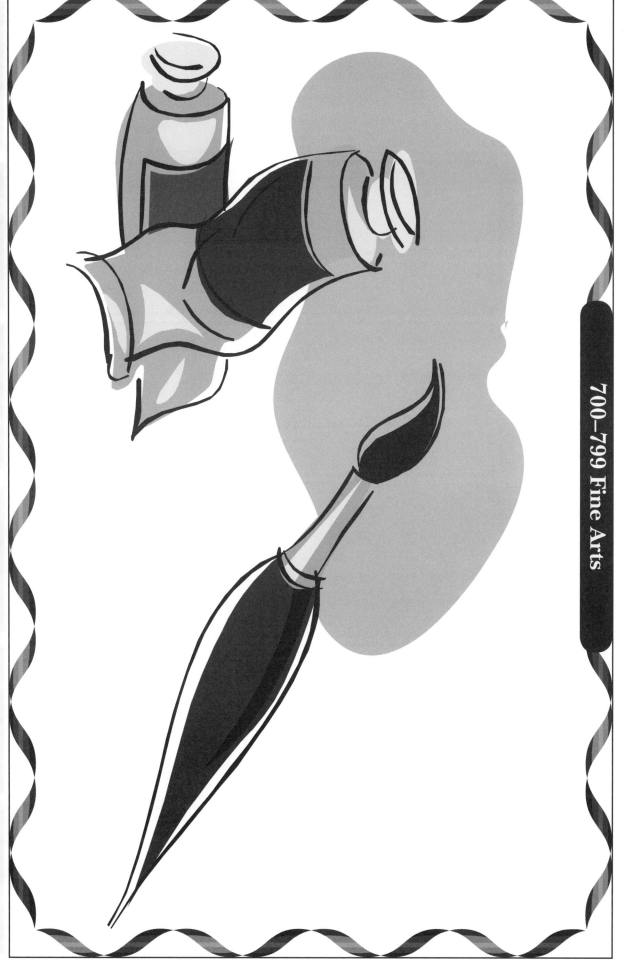

Nonfiction Spines Card Set 4 Picture Checker

Photocopy this picture onto the back of the spine cards on the previous page.

700–799 Fine Arts

Nonfiction Spines Card Set 5

Photocopy the picture on page 31 to the back of this page. Cut the spines apart. Students place the spines in order, then flip the pieces over to check their work. If the picture is correct, the spines are correct.

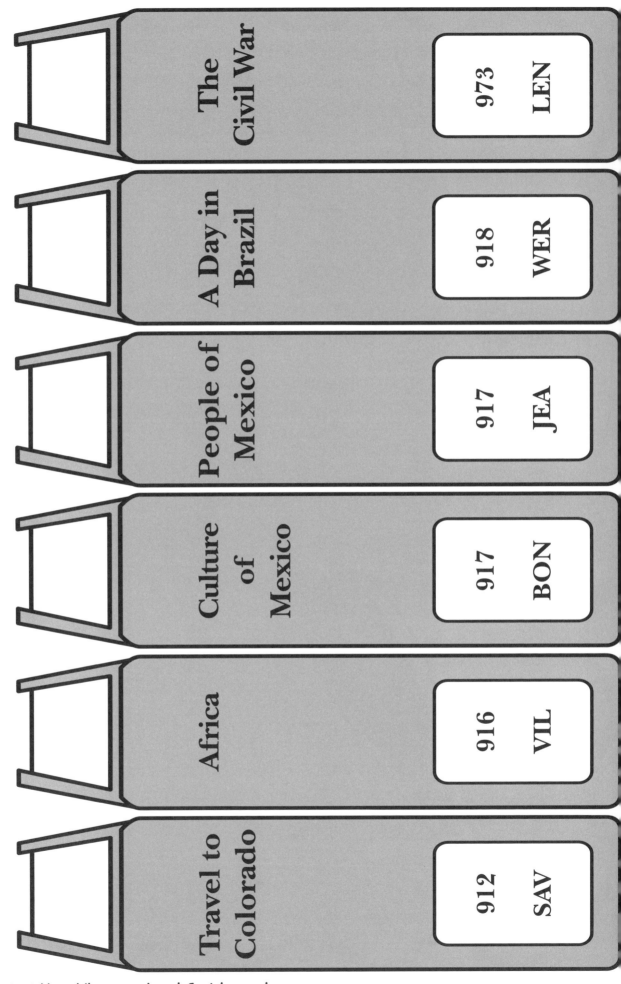

The
Civil War

973
LEN

A Day in
Brazil

918
WER

People of
Mexico

917
JEA

Culture
of
Mexico

917
BON

Africa

916
VIL

Travel to
Colorado

912
SAV

Nonfiction Spines Card Set 5 Picture Checker

Photocopy this picture onto the back of the spine cards on the previous page.

900–999 Geography, History

Categorizing Subjects

Library Strategies

- Understanding that similar topics within each Dewey hundreds category are grouped together
- Sorting three different topics within the 500s section

Materials Needed

- overhead of Subject Category Answer Sheet (page 33)
- Subject Category Card Sets—one set per pair of students (pages 34–36)

Time Needed

30 minutes

Directions

1. As a large group, review what has been learned in the last activities about the Dewey Decimal System.

2. Explain that this activity extends the categorizing of subjects within the 500s section.

3. The class will first practice by categorizing themselves. Establish areas for movement and where the groups will stand. For fun and warm-up, instruct the class to group themselves according to the following criteria:

   - those wearing: sneakers, open-toed shoes, all other shoes
   - those who: walked to school, came on two wheels, four wheels, more wheels
   - those who: like chocolate cake, those who don't
   - those who: have brothers/sisters, those who have none

   Explain that the next category attributes are similar to how the subjects in the nonfiction section are created. Use the following examples:

   - those who are animals and those who aren't
   - those who are boys and those who are girls
   - boys who watched television this morning and those who did not; girls who read a book this morning and those who didn't

4. Ask students to count the number of groups after each sorting. Note that the groups changed from a general grouping to a more specific grouping. Explain that in the Dewey Decimal System, that happens also.

5. Explain that the 500s section (Natural Sciences) contains many/varied topics about nature that are grouped together according to common characteristics.

6. Distribute the Subject Category Card Sets to each pair of students. Direct them to sort the topics into three piles. Choose one of the cards in each group as a heading.

7. When students finish, display the overhead of the Subject Category Answer Sheet. Allow time for students to make corrections and to ask for clarification.

Subject Category Answer Sheet

Wild Animals	Outer Space	Weather
Monkeys	Stars	Tornadoes
Bears	Planets	Clouds
Lizards	Moon	Hail Storms
Butterflies	Earth	Hurricanes
Birds	Comets	Blizzards

 Wild Animals

Monkeys

 Bears

 Lizards

 Butterflies

 Birds

 Outer Space

 Stars

 Planets

 The Moon

 The Earth

 Comets

 Weather

 Tornadoes

 Clouds

 Hail Storms

 Hurricanes

 Blizzards

Exploring the Nonfiction Shelves

Library Strategies

- Locating subject sections to locate wild animals, pets, sports, comics, drawing, dinosaurs, airplanes, rocks, volcanoes, weather, poetry, folklore

- Choosing a book

Materials Needed

- Dewey Decimal Chart (page 13)

- Exploring Nonfiction Cards—a set of 40 cards (pages 39–48)

- one shelf stick for each student

- lapboards

- pencil and lined paper

- transparency of "Choosing the Right Books" chart (page 38)

- examples of fiction and nonfiction books to demonstrate how to choose a book

Time Needed

45 minutes

Directions

1. Today students will physically explore the library to locate books in the different Dewey sections.

2. The task is to find a book about each topic listed on the Exploring Nonfiction Cards and write the title using correct capitalization and underlining.

3. Students number their paper from one to 40. Allow them to work in pairs, but everyone must write the titles of the books next to the corresponding number.

4. Students should use shelf sticks to hold the place for the book when it is pulled off the shelf.

5. Give each pair of students one card at a time and send them off to search for a book with the topic listed on the card. Allow students to use the Dewey Decimal Charts. When finished, students return the card to the teacher/librarian and get their answer checked before receiving another card. Allow 20–30 minutes to complete as many cards as possible.

6. Gather students back into the large group, collect papers, and discuss favorite sections of the library and/or interesting books they found during the search.

7. Finding a book doesn't always mean it is the best book to check out. Display both fiction and nonfiction books. Use the chart "Choosing the Right Book" and discuss the thought process used in determining if a book is a good choice.

Choosing the Right Books	
Fiction Books	**Nonfiction Books**
Use the five-finger method for readability. Read one page. If you cannot read or understand five words, then the book may be too difficult.	Look at the amount of words and pictures.
Read the blurb on the back of the book or on the inside flap. Does it sound interesting?	Ask yourself if the book will be read from cover to cover or if it will be used for browsing or research.
Consider the author. Is this an author whose books you have read before and liked?	Is the subject matter interesting to you?
Consider the opinions of your classmates.	Is it a book to be read by the student or will parents read it to the student?

Exploring Nonfiction Cards

1 Find a book about Spanish words.

2 Find a book about voting.

3 Find a book of mythology.

4 Find a book about a president.

6 Find a book about fire trucks.

8 Find a book of jump rope rhymes.

5 Find a book about Thanksgiving.

7 Find a book about the orchestra.

9

Find a book of poems.

11

Find a book about
a state.

10

Find a book about
Africa.

12

Find a book about
an artist.

13 Find a book about ghosts.

14 Find a book about birds.

15 Find a book about cards.

16 Find a book about how to take care of a puppy.

17 Find a book about gymnastics.

18 Find a book of recipes from a different country.

19 Find a book about newspapers.

20 Find a book about a famous athlete.

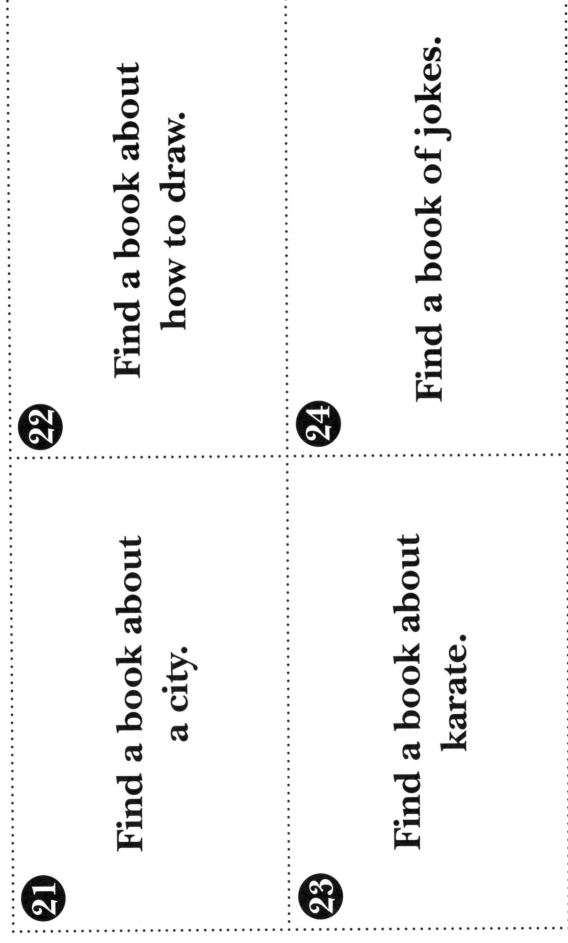

22 Find a book about how to draw.

24 Find a book of jokes.

21 Find a book about a city.

23 Find a book about karate.

25

Find a book about monkeys.

26

Find a book about airplanes.

27

Find a book about soccer.

28

Find a book of plays.

C–5

30 Find a book about cows.

32 Find a book about a Tyrannosaurus Rex.

29 Find a songbook.

31 Find a book about feelings.

33

Find a book about China.

34

Find a book about weather.

35

Find a book of folktales.

36

Find a book with many different facts.

38 Find a book about the history of the telephone.

40 Find a book about the human body.

37 Find a book about fishing.

39 Find a book about knitting or sewing.